School Feels DIFFERENT

Written by
Mandeesh Gill

To Rohan
For always being brave and resilient.
MG

Published in association with Bear With Us Productions

Illustrated by
Noor Alshalabi

School Feels DIFFERENT

Written by
Mandeesh Gill

"Come on, Rohan, you're going to be late!" Mum says as we hurry towards the school gate.

But **something has changed**, things don't feel right. There's a big sign next to school in black and white.

Mum reads from the sign and **puts her mask on carefully**.

I take her hand and we walk in, a little slowly.

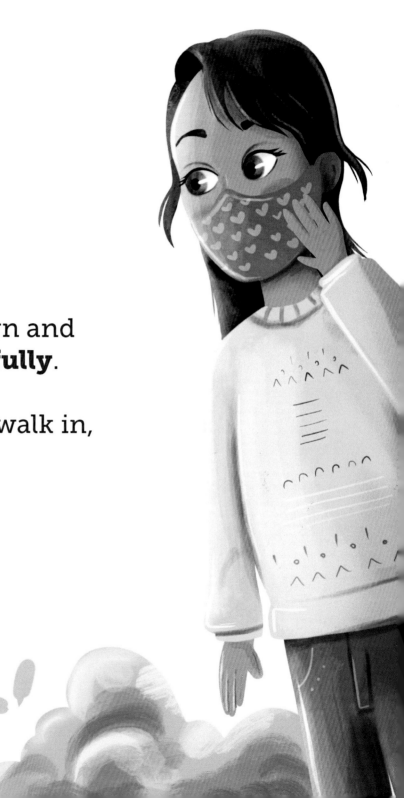

The playground **looks different**
with **yellow lines on the ground**.
I stand in the queue with Mum,
and look all around.

I start to **feel nervous**,
not sure what to expect.
Mum **squeezes my hand**, bends
down and gives me a gentle peck.

I wait for my teacher to open the door.
Then I say goodbye to Mum and march
towards the corridor.

I try my best to be **confident** and **strong**,
because I don't want to get into trouble
if I put a foot wrong.

My teacher **explains new rule after rule**,
which will help keep us **all safe**
during the day at school.

"Take off your coats and **wash your hands**.
Then sit at your desk, face forward
and don't stand."

I don't feel like school is
going to **be much fun**.
I wish I was going back
home with Mum.

We start the day with talking
about our **emotions** and **feelings,**
before we get on with mental
maths and guided reading.

We have to stay in **classroom bubbles**, and try not to mix,
With other classes, teachers and kids.

I miss Mark and Sophie in another bubble- my good mates,
but it's time for arts and crafts and I soon get stuck in with the paints.

At lunchtime, we eat at our
desks in our **classroom bubble**.
We can't mix in the canteen, it
will cause **Covid trouble**.

We choose what filling
we want in our bread,
but the dinner lady **got it wrong**
and gave me tuna instead.

I take a few bites
and like it, I think,
and wash it down with
my favourite drink.

The best part is the
chocolate chip cookie,
but eating it in one go
is a **little bit tricky**!

I rush my food to go **out to play**.

It's the only time we
can go **outside** in the day.

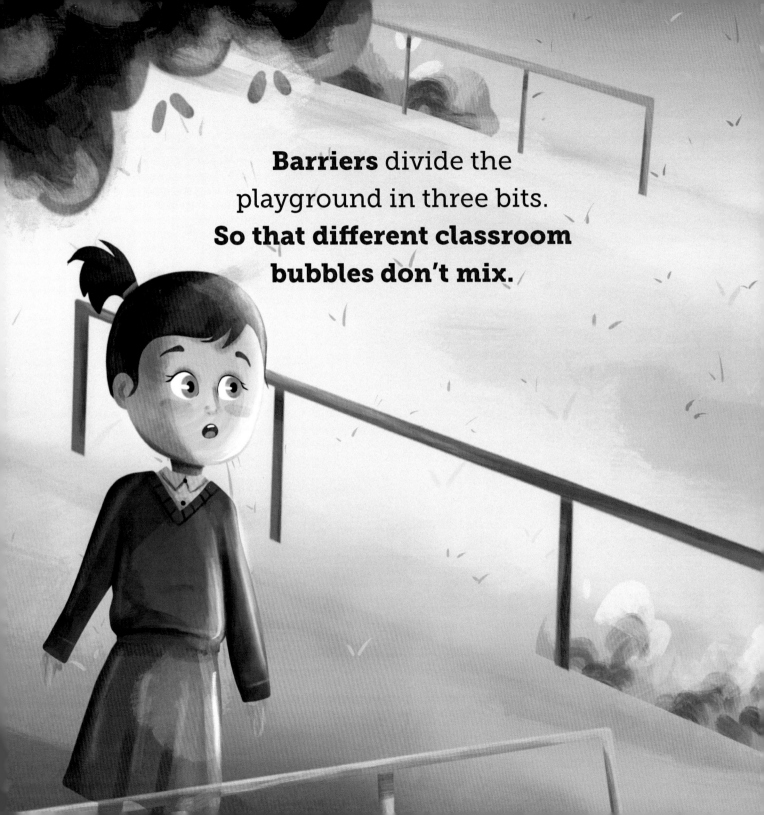

Barriers divide the playground in three bits. **So that different classroom bubbles don't mix.**

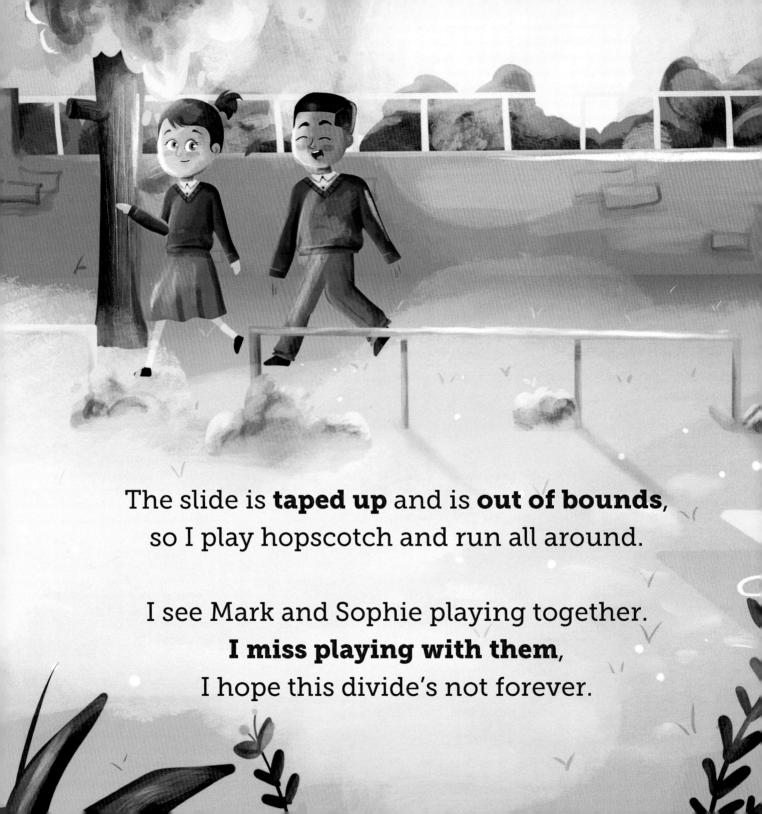

The slide is **taped up** and is **out of bounds**,
so I play hopscotch and run all around.

I see Mark and Sophie playing together.
I miss playing with them,
I hope this divide's not forever.

I start to enjoy myself with my new
classmates playing chase.
20 minutes go by at a very fast pace.

Playtime feels short but
we are **full of excitement**,
ready for the afternoon science experiment.

We get stuck in with glitter
snow globes and blue and
green lava lamps,
and exploding volcanoes
and fossil foot stamps.

We have created a big,
bold colourful scene.
**It's been a lot more fun than
I thought it would be.**

School is nearly finished
and we are asked to stand,

to go to the toilets and **wash our hands**.

We put on our coats and wait at our desks,
for parents to collect us,

I wave goodbye to my
teacher and my friends.
I can't wait to be back at school again.

To do science, arts and crafts and paints,
and play with my new classroom mates.

I run out of the door towards Mum,

and excitedly tell her **how much I've had fun.**

Mum smiles and says, "Come on, Rohan, **I'm taking you to the park**.

You're going to have a **playdate** with Sophie and Mark!"

2 m